Super Spelling tutor

(for ages 7-11)

Managing Editor: Simon Melhuish

Series Editor: Nikole G Bamford

Educational Advisor: Cathy Martin

Designer: Linley J Clode

Cover: Alan Shiner

Published by
The Lagoon Group
PO Box 311, KT2 5QW, UK
PO Box 990676, Boston, MA 02199, USA

ISBN: 1905439016

www.intelliquestbooks.com

Printed in China

IntelliQuest

UNIQUE BOOK CODE	054

Instructions

First of all make sure you have one of these Quizmos pictured here.

Find the book's unique code (this appears at the top of this page). Use the < and > buttons to scroll to this number on the Quizmo screen. Press the ⬥ button to enter the code, and you're ready to go. Use the < > scroll buttons to select the question number you want to answer. Press the Ⓐ, Ⓑ, Ⓒ, or Ⓓ button to enter your chosen answer.

If you are correct the green light beside the button you pressed will flash. You can then use the scroll button to move on to another question.

If your answer is incorrect, the red light beside the button you pressed will flash.

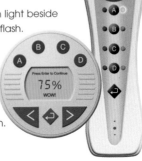

Don't worry, you can try again and again until you have the correct answer, OR move on to another question. (Beware: the more times you guess incorrectly, the lower your final percentage score will be!)

You can finish the quiz at any point — just press the ⬅ button to find out your score and rank as follows:

75% or above	You're the spelling bee's knees!
50% — 74%	You're on the way to being a spelling star.
25% — 49%	Try harder — you'll get there.
Less than 25%	You just need to try, try again and you'll spell success!

If you do press the ⬅ button to find out your score, this will end your session and you will have to use the ⬅ to start again!

HAVE FUN!

INTRODUCTION

Have fun learning to spell with this book. We have over 400 questions which give you four versions of how to spell a word. There will only be one correct spelling and you have to work out which one it is.

The age range for this is 7-11 year olds so if you're 7 and you don't score brilliantly then don't worry. Just keep coming back to the book and learn by redoing the quiz.

You 11 year olds should know all these words and knowing them will help you get great grades at school and pass all your spelling tests.

Good Luck and Have Fun.

This is suitable for all kids. If you're 7 or 8 you should be able to tackle most of these words and if you're 9 and above these should be relatively easy.

001

- **A** hous
- **B** hows
- **C** house
- **D** huose

002

- **A** from
- **B** frome
- **C** fom
- **D** frum

003

- **A** jrink
- **B** drnik
- **C** drink
- **D** drinck

004

- **A** tabel
- **B** tabl
- **C** tabol
- **D** table

005

A cher **B** chiar

C chair **D** chere

006

A happy **B** happe

C hapy **D** hapee

007

A rabit **B** rabbit

C rabat **D** rabt

008

A out **B** owt

C oute **D** owte

009

A bal **B** bol

C ball **D** boll

010

A good   **B** gud

C gude   **D** goode

011

A fli   **B** fliy

C fly   **D** flye

012

A bote   **B** boat

C bot   **D** bowt

013

A cum   **B** come

C cume   **D** com

014

A dor   **B** dore

C door   **D** doore

015

A dus

B deos

C does

D doese

016

A gerl

B girl

C gurl

D gril

017

A meny

B many

C menny

D manny

018

A anemal

B animl

C animal

D anemol

019

A ask

B arsk

C arsck

D acks

020

A beter

B bettre

C betr

D better

021

A berthday

B birthday

C brithday

D burthday

022

A Wednesday

B Wensday

C Wendsday

D Wednseday

023

A yelo

B yello

C yellowe

D yellow

024

A head

B hed

C haed

D heade

025

A partey   **B** praty

C party   **D** partee

026

A vidio   **B** viddyo

C video   **D** vidyo

027

A sorry   **B** sorre

C sorrey   **D** surry

028

A summr   **B** summer

C sumer   **D** summa

029

A going   **B** gowing

C goeing   **D** gowng

030

A bird　　　　**B** berd

C brid　　　　**D** birde

031

A thanke　　　　**B** thanck

C thancke　　　　**D** thank

032

A once　　　　**B** onse

C wuns　　　　**D** wons

033

A bleu　　　　**B** blu

C blou　　　　**D** blue

034

A pensul　　　　**B** pensal

C pencil　　　　**D** pensle

035
- **A** abowt
- **B** about
- **C** aboat
- **D** abuot

036
- **A** bruther
- **B** brotha
- **C** brother
- **D** bruthr

037
- **A** sik
- **B** sicke
- **C** sike
- **D** sick

038
- **A** tidey
- **B** tiddy
- **C** tiedy
- **D** tidy

039
- **A** money
- **B** munny
- **C** muney
- **D** monny

040

A luckey   **B** lukky

C lucky   **D** luccy

041

A worter   **B** watter

C warter   **D** water

042

A frend   **B** freind

C friend   **D** frende

043

A shuold   **B** shud

C should   **D** shood

044

A becuase   **B** becos

C becoz   **D** because

045

A eigt

B eight

C eigth

D ait

046

A Awgusd

B August

C Awgust

D Augusd

047

A lauf

B larf

C laugh

D largh

048

A onest

B honist

C onist

D honest

049

A babbeis

B babies

C babyes

D babys

050

A talkeing   B torking

C talkin   D talking

051

A bath   B baff

C barth   D bafth

052

A pleyground   B playgrownd

C playground   D pleygrownd

053

A bubbel   B bubel

C bubble   D buble

054

A kleen   B clean

C klean   D cleen

055
- **A** schule
- **B** school
- **C** scool
- **D** skool

056
- **A** making
- **B** makeing
- **C** mayking
- **D** maiking

057
- **A** jjeens
- **B** jeanz
- **C** jeans
- **D** geans

058
- **A** chickin
- **B** chikkin
- **C** chicking
- **D** chicken

059
- **A** teecha
- **B** teacha
- **C** teacher
- **D** teecher

If you're 7 or 8 these words may be a little too hard but come back to them and you'll soon master them. They should still be OK for you 9 and overs.

060

A granmutha

B granmother

C grandmother

D grammother

061

A beootiful

B beautiful

C beautifull

D buteiful

062

A leaves

B leeves

C leevs

D leavs

063

A mobeil

B mobil

C mobile

D mobel

064

A. libary   B. library

C. librery   D. libery

065

A. February   B. Febuary

C. Febury   D. Februrary

066

A. bisickle   B. bicicle

C. bisicle   D. bicycle

067

A. moden   B. modarn

C. moddern   D. modern

068

A. gobel   B. gobbel

C. gobble   D. goble

069

A breakeble   **B** braikable

C breakible   **D** breakable

070

A braikfast   **B** breakfest

C brekfast   **D** breakfast

071

A dreiming   **B** dreaming

C dreeming   **D** dreaming

072

A oshen   **B** osean

C oshan   **D** ocean

073

A greasy   **B** greazy

C greesy   **D** greezy

074
- **A** spesial
- **B** special
- **C** speshul
- **D** speshal

075
- **A** weakend
- **B** wekend
- **C** weekend
- **D** weikend

076
- **A** skeliton
- **B** skelleton
- **C** skeleton
- **D** skeleten

077
- **A** safety
- **B** safetee
- **C** safty
- **D** saftie

078
- **A** different
- **B** diffrent
- **C** differant
- **D** diffrant

079
- **A** vedgetable
- **B** vegtable
- **C** vegetable
- **D** vegtabel

080
- **A** mighte
- **B** miht
- **C** might
- **D** meit

081
- **A** signel
- **B** signal
- **C** signil
- **D** signell

082
- **A** voise
- **B** voice
- **C** vuice
- **D** vois

083
- **A** sciense
- **B** siense
- **C** science
- **D** sciance

084
- **A** quiat
- **B** kwyat
- **C** quiet
- **D** quiut

085
- **A** breit
- **B** briht
- **C** brite
- **D** bright

086
- **A** haite
- **B** height
- **C** hieght
- **D** hite

087
- **A** brite
- **B** breit
- **C** bright
- **D** briht

088
- **A** wate
- **B** weight
- **C** waite
- **D** waight

089

A frightning

B fritening

C freitening

D frightening

090

A childood

B childhud

C childhood

D childehood

091

A clime

B cleim

C cleim

D climb

092

A shining

B shyning

C sheining

D shineing

093

A knieves

B kneives

C nives

D knives

094

A driving

B driveing

C drivving

D dryving

095

A lickeing

B likeing

C liking

D likking

096

A islend

B iland

C island

D ilend

097

A relation

B relaytion

C relasion

D relaysion

098

A soljier

B soljer

C soldier

D soldeir

099

A tellephone   **B** tellyfone

C telefone   **D** telephone

100

A tellyvision   **B** tellevision

C television   **D** televisian

101

A belief   **B** beleif

C beleef   **D** beleiff

102

A foke   **B** folk

C folke   **D** focke

103

A wallet   **B** wallat

C wallut   **D** wallit

104
A rember

B rimember

C remember

D rimembar

105
A somewhere

B sumware

C sumwhere

D someware

106
A tommorrow

B tomorow

C tomorrow

D tommorow

107
A hanbag

B handbag

C handbagg

D hanbagg

108
A wunder

B wonder

C wonda

D wunda

109

A candel

B candell

C candle

D candall

110

A sanwich

B sanwitch

C sandwich

D sandwitch

111

A lonly

B lonely

C loanly

D lonley

112

A runnin

B running

C runing

D runneng

113

A clockweise

B clokwise

C clockwise

D clockwize

114

A chocolate   B choclate

C chocklatt   D choclit

115

A broaken   B broeken

C brokan   D broken

116

A stumach   B stomach

C stummack   D stomick

117

A people   B peepel

C peopol   D peeple

118

A stopt   B stoped

C stoppd   D stopped

119
A sword
B sord
C soard
D sorde

120
A fata
B fater
C fatter
D fatta

121
A fotocopy
B fotacopy
C photocopy
D photacopy

122
A photograph
B photagraph
C fotograph
D fotagraph

123
A cubbard
B cupboard
C cuboard
D cuppard

124

A happened

B hapenned

C hapend

D happenned

125

A right

B righte

C riht

D reit

126

A morening

B moning

C mawning

D morning

127

A horrible

B horibel

C horribel

D horrabel

128

A fawty

B fourty

C fortey

D forty

129

A lisenning   B listning

C listening   D lissoning

130

A ansa   B answer

C arnser   D ahnsa

131

A mathmatics   B mathmatiks

C mathematics   D mathamatics

132

A kettel   B ketle

C ketel   D kettle

133

A Sataday   B Satterday

C Sattaday   D Saturday

134

A daughter **B** daurter

C dawter **D** daughta

135

A coud **B** cood

C could **D** cuod

136

A thurm **B** thum

C thumm **D** thumb

137

A grumbell **B** grumbel

C grumble **D** grumbal

138

A suasage **B** sosage

C sausage **D** sausige

139

A luvly   **B** lovly

C loveley   **D** lovely

140

A infented   **B** invented

C inventid   **D** innvented

141

A anywon   **B** anyone

C anywun   **D** annyone

142

A puppys   **B** pupies

C puppies   **D** puppees

143

A swiming   **B** swimmin

C swimmeng   **D** swimming

If you're 10 and over these should be OK. They might be tricky for the rest of you but keep on trying.

144

A blackbored

B blackboard

C blackbord

D blackborde

145

A reacsion

B reactian

C reaxion

D reaction

146

A against

B aginst

C ageinst

D agenst

147

A gellous

B gealous

C jealous

D jelluss

148

A healthe   **B** helth

C health   **D** halth

149

A shamefull   **B** shameful

C shaimfull   **D** shaimful

150

A granma   **B** grammar

C granmer   **D** grammer

151

A example   **B** egsample

C ecsample   **D** egsampel

152

A abandonned   **B** abandenned

C abandoned   **D** abandinned

153

A transaxion B transacsian

C transacshen D transaction

154

A trancepareant B transparant

C transparent D transparint

155

A meanwile B meenwhile

C meanwhile D meenwile

156

A gard B guard

C gaurd D garde

157

A swarm B sworm

C swarn D swarem

158

A direy

B diery

C diary

D deiry

159

A weery

B weary

C weiry

D weerey

160

A unavoidable

B unervoidable

C unavoidabel

D unervoidabel

161

A dette

B det

C dett

D debt

162

A subtracsion

B subtraxion

C subtracshan

D subtraction

163

A incapabel **B** inkapable

C incapable **D** incapeable

164

A ecschange **B** egschange

C exchainge **D** exchange

165

A ruff **B** rugh

C rouff **D** rough

166

A diside **B** decide

C deside **D** dicide

167

A nukkle **B** knuckel

C nuckle **D** knuckle

168

A decimal   B desimal

C decimel   D desimel

169

A lukkiest   B luckiest

C luckyest   D luckyist

170

A alcahol   B alcol

C alcohol   D alcool

171

A lokomotiv   B locamotive

C locomotive   D locamotif

172

A decompose   B deecompoze

C decompoze   D deecompose

173

A secondary **B** secondry

C secondery **D** secundry

174

A decrative **B** decratif

C decorative **D** decarative

175

A incredibel **B** incredebel

C incredible **D** incredeble

176

A secertary **B** secretary

C secretry **D** secretery

177

A mikroskope **B** microscope

C mikerscope **D** micrascope

178
- **A** dictionry
- **B** dictionery
- **C** dictionary
- **D** dicsionery

179
- **A** indeecent
- **B** indesent
- **C** indecent
- **D** indesant

180
- **A** medesine
- **B** medecine
- **C** medisine
- **D** medicine

181
- **A** awdianse
- **B** audience
- **C** audiense
- **D** audiance

182
- **A** awdition
- **B** audision
- **C** audition
- **D** ordition

183

- **A** riduced
- **B** reduced
- **C** ridused
- **D** redused

184

- **A** creasion
- **B** creashen
- **C** creatian
- **D** creation

185

- **A** neese
- **B** neice
- **C** niece
- **D** neece

186

- **A** spesific
- **B** spisific
- **C** spicific
- **D** specific

187

- **A** spectacular
- **B** spectaclar
- **C** spectaculer
- **D** spectacler

188

A spectater   B spectata

C specteter   D spectator

189

A therefore   B therfore

C therefor   D therefour

190

A enegy   B energi

C energy   D enirgy

191

A gess   B ghuess

C guess   D ghess

192

A pressure   B pressire

C preshure   D preshar

193

A afektion

B affecsion

C affection

D affeksion

194

A referance

B refrence

C refrance

D reference

195

A unfortunatly

B unfortuneately

C unfortunately

D unforchunately

196

A unfriendly

B unfrendly

C unfreindly

D unfrenly

197

A engagemint

B engagement

C engaugement

D engagment

198

A magician   B magishan

C majician   D majizian

199

A bigining   B begining

C beginning   D biginning

200

A signature   B signichure

C signiture   D signatcha

201

A argumint   B argumant

C argument   D arguemint

202

A cought   B caught

C caut   D cawt

203

A evedense

B evidence

C evidense

D evedence

204

A sheild

B sheeld

C shield

D sheald

205

A sientific

B psientific

C scientific

D scientifec

206

A flys

B flies

C fleis

D flyes

207

A thiefs

B thieves

C thievs

D theives

208

A eriginal   **B** originle

C original   **D** oridginal

209

A ceiling   **B** cieling

C seiling   **D** sieling

210

A primeate   **B** prymate

C primait   **D** primate

211

A rinkel   **B** wrinkle

C rinkle   **D** wrinkel

212

A union   **B** younion

C unian   **D** yunian

213

A writtin **B** ritten

C rittin **D** written

214

A adjective **B** adgective

C ajective **D** addjectiv

215

A beleive **B** beleife

C believe **D** beliefe

216

A deelighted **B** delited

C delighted **D** deelited

217

A pollinate **B** pollenate

C polinate **D** polenate

218

A colam   **B** column

C colum   **D** colamn

219

A women   **B** wimmin

C wommen   **D** wimen

220

A similar   **B** similler

C simmiler   **D** simmilar

221

A dominnoes   **B** dominos

C domminos   **D** dominoes

222

A comma   **B** comna

C commer   **D** comer

223

A reduxion   **B** reducsion

C riduction   **D** reduction

224

A fameous   **B** fameus

C famous   **D** feymuss

225

A competision   **B** competition

C competisian   **D** compitition

226

A concentrasion   **B** consentration

C concentration   **D** concentrashen

227

A dandeline   **B** dandylion

C dandilion   **D** dandelion

228

A hankerchief

B handkercheif

C hankercheif

D handkerchief

229

A beneath

B beneith

C bineath

D bineeth

230

A nuntheless

B nontheless

C nonetheless

D nonethaless

231

A confusian

B confucion

C confuzion

D confusion

232

A funiest

B funnyest

C funniest

D funnyesd

233

A noncence **B** noncense

C nonsense **D** nonsinse

234

A annule **B** anual

C anule **D** annual

235

A conveeniant **B** convenient

C conveneient **D** conveniant

236

A bony **B** boney

C bonye **D** boeny

237

A abored **B** aborde

C aboard **D** abord

238

A proseed

B prosede

C procede

D proceed

239

A prosiss

B process

C prosess

D prociss

240

A blockidge

B blockige

C blockedge

D blockage

241

A geography

B jography

C jograffy

D geogrephy

242

A swolen

B suolen

C swollen

D swolan

243

A emoshun   **B** emosion

C emotion   **D** emotian

244

A enouff   **B** enough

C enuff   **D** inough

245

A thaught   **B** thought

C thawt   **D** thaut

246

A shoulder   **B** shoaldar

C shoalder   **D** shouldar

247

A knowlige   **B** knolidge

C knowledge   **D** noledge

248
- **A** seperate
- **B** seprate
- **C** sepirate
- **D** separate

249
- **A** ripeat
- **B** ripeet
- **C** repeat
- **D** repeet

250
- **A** replacemint
- **B** replaicement
- **C** replacement
- **D** replaicemint

251
- **A** explenation
- **B** explanation
- **C** explenasion
- **D** explanasion

252
- **A** impossible
- **B** impossibel
- **C** imposibel
- **D** imposible

253

A emptyness

B emptiniss

C emptiness

D emptyniss

254

A strayght

B straight

C strayt

D strate

255

A electricity

B electrisity

C elektrisity

D electrissity

256

A cairlessness

B carlessness

C cairlissniss

D carelessness

257

A shurly

B shurley

C shorly

D surely

258
A strenth B strengthe

C strength D strenthe

259
A morover B maurover

C morova D moreover

260
A marjarine B margerine

C margarin D margarine

261
A forgiveable B forgivable

C foregivabel D forgivaball

262
A varyety B variaty

C varriety D variety

263

A purify

B purifie

C pureefy

D pureify

264

A thrugh

B through

C throgh

D thrue

265

A suprise

B serprise

C surprise

D suprize

266

A marrige

B mariage

C marriage

D maridge

267

A berries

B burys

C beries

D berrys

268

A portable   B portibell

C portible   D portabal

269

A furthamore   B ferthermore

C furthermore   D ferthamore

270

A certificite   B certificat

C certificate   D cirtificet

271

A survay   B survey

C servey   D servay

272

A nervus   B nervous

C nerrvos   D nerverse

273

A missbehave   B missbeehave

C misbehave   D misbeehave

274

A discovry   B discuvery

C discovery   D discuvry

275

A discribe   B diskribe

C diskreib   D describe

276

A dissgusting   B disgusting

C discusting   D discussting

277

A dizine   B desine

C design   D dessine

278

A rasperry

B raspberry

C rasberry

D rassberry

279

A missteak

B misstake

C misteak

D mistake

280

A distrebution

B distribusion

C distribution

D distrebusion

281

A ishoe

B ishue

C issew

D issue

282

A insulation

B insolasion

C insulasion

D insolation

283

- **A** octagen
- **B** octogon
- **C** octargon
- **D** octagon

284

- **A** interesting
- **B** intresting
- **C** intressting
- **D** inntresting

285

- **A** matteriel
- **B** matterial
- **C** material
- **D** materiall

286

- **A** althogh
- **B** altho
- **C** although
- **D** allthough

287

- **A** notice
- **B** knowtis
- **C** notiss
- **D** notise

288

A alltogether   **B** alltogetha

C altogether   **D** alltogever

289

A astronommy   **B** astronnomy

C astronamy   **D** astronomy

290

A fattning   **B** fattenin

C fattening   **D** fatning

291

A pattern   **B** patern

C pattan   **D** patturn

292

A lettace   **B** lettuce

C lettus   **D** lettice

293

A actually   **B** actully

C atchally   **D** atchually

294

A aqaurium   **B** acquarium

C aquarium   **D** aquarioum

295

A rhubarb   **B** roobarb

C rubharb   **D** rubarbe

296

A edducation   **B** eddication

C education   **D** educasion

297

A tutched   **B** touched

C toucht   **D** tuched

298

A chuckel   **B** chuckle

C chukkle   **D** chukle

299

A lauffed   **B** larfed

C laughed   **D** laffed

300

A woond   **B** wunde

C wound   **D** woonde

301

A boundry   **B** boundary

C boundery   **D** bowndary

302

A jurney   **B** journey

C jurnay   **D** jerny

303
A unusuel **B** unusule

C unusual **D** unnusuel

304
A development **B** developmant

C developmint **D** develapmant

305
A reveiw **B** rivue

C riview **D** review

306
A envireonment **B** environment

C enviroment **D** envirament

307
A royalty **B** roylety

C roylty **D** royelty

308

A physicle
B physikle
C fysical
D physical

309

A manager
B managar
C maneger
D mannager

310

A tempriture
B temprature
C temperature
D tempratare

311

A dissappoint
B disapoint
C disappoint
D dissapoint

312

A disobey
B dissobey
C disobay
D dissobay

This is the toughest section. Whatever your age have a go. Don't worry if the words are too difficult. You'll get better with practice.

313

A autograff

B autograph

C autagraph

D autagraff

314

A peaceful

B piecefull

C pieceful

D peacefull

315

A practice

B practiss

C praktise

D practisce

316

A imajinry

B imaginry

C imaginery

D imaginary

317
- **A** evaluation
- **B** ivaluation
- **C** evaluasion
- **D** ivaluasian

318
- **A** dimand
- **B** diamand
- **C** diemond
- **D** diamond

319
- **A** champyenship
- **B** champianship
- **C** championship
- **D** champyonship

320
- **A** graffik
- **B** graphic
- **C** grafic
- **D** graffic

321
- **A** stationry
- **B** stasionry
- **C** stationary
- **D** stasionary

322

A innatentive **B** innattentive

C inatentive **D** inattentive

323

A embaras **B** embarras

C embarass **D** embarrass

324

A publication **B** publicasian

C publicatian **D** publicasion

325

A suxessful **B** sucksessful

C successful **D** successfull

326

A diceased **B** disseased

C deceised **D** deceased

327

A riseed B receed

C recede D resede

328

A diseat B deseet

C deceit D deciet

329

A reseeve B recieve

C resieve D receive

330

A grabd B grabbed

C grabed D grabt

331

A teknik B technique

C tekneek D tecneque

332

A tecnology

B tecnologie

C technology

D tecknology

333

A anshient

B ainshent

C ancent

D ancient

334

A dicision

B decision

C desizion

D disizion

335

A accomodation

B acommodation

C acomodation

D accommodation

336

A secretively

B secritively

C secrtivelee

D secritiveley

337

A escursion

B excurtion

C excursion

D excersion

338

A awdibel

B audibel

C audible

D audibal

339

A auditoriam

B auditorium

C orditorium

D awditoriam

340

A industryal

B industrial

C industriell

D industriall

341

A precaution

B pricausion

C precausian

D pricaution

342

A electrisian **B** electrition

C electrician **D** electrision

343

A prehistorik **B** prihistoric

C preistoric **D** prehistoric

344

A premetuer **B** premiture

C premature **D** premachar

345

A plentifull **B** plentyfull

C plentiful **D** plentyful

346

A preperation **B** preparation

C preperasion **D** preparasian

347

A. fierce

B. fearce

C. fearse

D. feirce

348

A. priscription

B. priscripsion

C. prescription

D. prescripshen

349

A. infexious

B. infectious

C. infexius

D. infecsiuss

350

A. definite

B. defenet

C. definate

D. definet

351

A. acquatic

B. aqautic

C. akwatic

D. aquatic

352

A signifikant　　**B** significkent

C significent　　**D** significant

353

A rehersel　　**B** rehersal

C rehearsal　　**D** rihersal

354

A wierd　　**B** weerd

C weard　　**D** weird

355

A poisenous　　**B** poisnous

C poisanuss　　**D** poisonous

356

A illedgible　　**B** illegible

C illegable　　**D** illegibal

357

A billingule

B bylingual

C billinguall

D bilingual

358

A voluntary

B volantry

C volantary

D voluntery

359

A immachure

B immature

C imature

D imatchar

360

A demenstrasion

B demenstration

C demonstration

D demunstrasion

361

A memrable

B memarable

C memorable

D memarabell

362

A atmosphere   **B** atmosfear

C atmosfere   **D** atmasphere

363

A competitive   **B** competative

C compatative   **D** compitive

364

A compleshan   **B** complesion

C completion   **D** complesian

365

A simplissity   **B** simplisity

C simplicity   **D** simpalicity

366

A composision   **B** composition

C compasition   **D** compersisian

367

A sinsearly   **B** sincerely

C sinserely   **D** sincerley

368

A concluesion   **B** conclusian

C conclusion   **D** conclewsion

369

A unecessary   **B** unnecessery

C unnecessary   **D** unnessessary

370

A jenerus   **B** genarous

C generus   **D** generous

371

A miniture   **B** miniature

C minature   **D** minacher

372

A consiquence   **B** concequence

C consequence   **D** consiquense

373

A continuas   **B** continuous

C continuess   **D** continous

374

A mannuscript   **B** manuescript

C manuscripped   **D** manuscript

375

A proffession   **B** professian

C profession   **D** profeshan

376

A peerce   **B** pearce

C pearse   **D** pierce

377

A abominable **B** abomnabal

C abomnable **D** abomnebel

378

A frunteer **B** fronteir

C fronteer **D** frontier

379

A proportion **B** proporsion

C praportian **D** preporsion

380

A propasition **B** propersition

C proposition **D** proposision

381

A drowt **B** drout

C drought **D** droute

382

A especially   **B** espeshly

C espeshally   **D** especialy

383

A unpleazant   **B** unpleasent

C unpleasant   **D** unplessent

384

A repleca   **B** replicar

C replika   **D** replica

385

A egsplosion   **B** exploshen

C explosion   **D** ecsplozion

386

A opposition   **B** opposision

C oppasision   **D** oppersition

387
- **A** improbible
- **B** improbable
- **C** improbibal
- **D** improbabel

388
- **A** improvise
- **B** improvize
- **C** imporvise
- **D** impravise

389
- **A** sequense
- **B** seequince
- **C** sequence
- **D** sequince

390
- **A** enquire
- **B** enkwire
- **C** enquier
- **D** enquyre

391
- **A** parrallel
- **B** paralell
- **C** parallel
- **D** parralell

392

A stratagy **B** strategy

C stratergy **D** stratagie

393

A cercumstance **B** circumstance

C sircumstance **D** sercumstanse

394

A performanse **B** performence

C performance **D** performense

395

A varyasion **B** varyation

C variation **D** variasian

396

A buryed **B** buried

C buryde **D** beryed

397

A. shreik   B. shriek

C. shreek   D. shreke

398

A. permanant   B. permenint

C. permanent   D. permenent

399

A. corrosion   B. corrosian

C. corrossion   D. corrosian

400

A. ferrie   B. furrie

C. fewry   D. furry

401

A. pursuade   B. persuade

C. persuede   D. pursuede

402

A mortgage   B morgidge

C morgage   D morgige

403

A parsiel   B partiel

C parshal   D partial

404

A particular   B patticular

C particuler   D paticuler

405

A dissappear   B dissapear

C disappear   D dissapere

406

A mischeif   B mischeef

C mischief   D misscheif

407

A muscle

B musle

C musel

D muscel

408

A discription

B description

C discripsion

D descripshen

409

A research

B resurch

C reserch

D resertch

410

A assessment

B assesment

C asessment

D assesmant

411

A musicien

B musisian

C musizion

D musician

412

A business

B bussiness

C bizness

D bisnass

413

A dissobediant

B disobediant

C disabedient

D disobedient

414

A risources

B resourses

C resources

D resawces

415

A suspision

B suspicion

C suspishon

D susspician

416

A responsibel

B risponsible

C responsible

D responsable

417
- **A** desqualify
- **B** diskwalify
- **C** desqualifie
- **D** disqualify

418
- **A** disatisfyed
- **B** disatisfied
- **C** dissatasfied
- **D** dissatisfied

419
- **A** attention
- **B** attension
- **C** atension
- **D** attenshan

420
- **A** dissapprove
- **B** dissaproove
- **C** disapprove
- **D** dissaprove

421
- **A** alternativley
- **B** alternativally
- **C** alturnatively
- **D** alternatively

422

A interuppt **B** interupt

C interrupt **D** intarupt

423

A antedote **B** auntidote

C antidote **D** antidowt

424

A pashent **B** patiant

C pasient **D** patient

425

A arteficial **B** artificial

C artifishell **D** artefisial

426

A anteseptic **B** antiseptic

C antyseptik **D** anteseptik

427
- **A** awtobiograffy
- **B** autobiogrephy
- **C** autobiography
- **D** ortobiograffy

428
- **A** awtomobile
- **B** autamobeel
- **C** automobele
- **D** automobile

429
- **A** outragious
- **B** outrageous
- **C** owtrageous
- **D** outrajuss

430
- **A** bouh
- **B** bouw
- **C** bau
- **D** bough

431
- **A** cough
- **B** coff
- **C** couff
- **D** cogh

432

A baught   B baut

C bought   D baurt

433

A taurt   B tought

C taught   D taute

434

A jernalist   B journalist

C jurnalisd   D jernalissed

435

A nauzea   B nausea

C nawsea   D nausia

436

A revolution   B revolusion

C revalusion   D revalutian

437

A rithmic   **B** rythmic

C rhythmic   **D** rhithmic

438

A dimention   **B** dimensian

C diamention   **D** dimension

439

A perspecktive   **B** purspective

C perspective   **D** paspective

440

A encurrage   **B** encurridge

C encourage   **D** encurage

441

A possesion   **B** possession

C posesion   **D** posession

Other Titles

There are many other exciting quiz
and puzzle books in the IntelliQuest range,
and your QUIZMO electronic unit
knows the answers to them all!

You can order from your
local bookshop or online bookseller.

For a full listing of current titles
(and ISBN numbers) see:

www.intelliquestbooks.com

LAGOON
BOOKS